TEACHING PRACTICE

D0676204

WITHDRAWN

Danny goes to school

Adapted by: Pamela Egan
Pictures: Dea de Vries

242088

Church Information Office
Church House, Dean's Yard, London SW1P 3NZ

Tomorrow
Danny goes to school
for the first time.
Danny is glad
but he feels a bit funny
all the same.
What will school be like?

Mum says,
'I will take you to school
on my way to work.
I will be waiting outside
at going-home time.
You can take sandwiches
and an apple
for your dinner.'

Danny asks,
'Will there be a lot of children?'
'Yes,' says Mum,
'but you will soon get to know them.'
Danny doesn't ask Mum
if the children like school.
But he wonders.

Danny asks,
'Do you know the teacher?'
'Oh, yes' says Mum.

Danny doesn't ask Mum
if the teacher is kind or cross.
But he wonders.

Today
Danny goes to school
for the very first time!
He feels a bit funny.
He doesn't ask Mum
if the other children
are all very big.
But he wonders.

Mum takes Danny to school.
Here's the teacher, Miss Green.
Danny holds his Mum's hand.
Miss Green says
'Hello, Danny!
It's lovely to meet you.
Come and meet the others.'

'Children, this is Danny,'
says Miss Green.
'He has come to play with us.'
Danny looks at the children.
No, they are not very big.
They are about as big as Danny.
Not bigger.

A boy says,
'I'm Jason.'
Another says,
'I'm Mick. I know you!'
'And I know you!' says Danny.
Danny and Mick
often meet in the park.

Jason is making a tower.
Danny asks, ‘Do you like school?’
‘Mostly I do,’ says Jason.
‘I like playtime
and stories
and painting
and playing the drum in the band.’
‘Wow!’ says Danny.
‘Is that what we do?’ he thinks.

Miss Green and the children
make up a story.
Danny helps.
Miss Green smiles at Danny.
She has a kind face –
not a cross face.

Now it's dinner-time.
Danny has his sandwiches
and his apple.
Mick has a banana.
Danny says, 'Monkeys like bananas.'
'Well, I'm a monkey,' says Mick.
He swings his arms and makes a fac
Danny giggles.

'Put your coat on, Danny,'
says Miss Green.
'It's not time to go home,
is it?' says Danny.
'Not yet,' says Miss Green.
'We are going to play outside.'

Danny and Mick and Jason
all have rides in a cart.
They take turns to pull it.

Here's Mum!
Danny has lots to tell her.
'Goodbye, Danny' calls Miss Green.
'Goodbye, Miss Green. See
you tomorrow!'

CHRIST CHURCH COLLEGE CANTERBURY

Notes for parents and teachers:

This Benjamin Book is one of a series which deals with children's important experiences – going to school for the first time, having a country holiday, moving house, going to hospital, getting a new baby in the family, having a birthday. (It may be helpful to know that *Joe has a new house* is about a one-parent family.)

They can be used just as a basis for shared talk and discussion about these experiences, some of which can be disturbing for young children. These stories allow them a chance to question and give adults the opportunity to help and reassure them. But the stories can also be used, if you so wish, as part of religious teaching. The wonders of God's world, people who help us, the joys of friendship and sharing are implicit in the stories and can be linked to religious teaching or lead into prayers related to the children's own needs.

Produced by arrangement with Nederlandsche Zondagsschool Vereeniging Amsterdam.

© English Text: Central Board of Finance of the Church of England, 1978.